In Hell... Everyone Eats Watermelon NAKED

A LONG OVERDUE BOOK

John Long

POCKET BOOKS

New York   London   Toronto   Sydney   Tokyo   Singapore

The cartoons on the cover and in this book have been previously published in syndication and distributed by King Features Syndicate.

An *Original* publication of POCKET BOOKS

POCKET BOOKS, a division of Simon & Schuster Inc.
1230 Avenue of the Americas, New York, NY 10020

Dedicated to my daughter
Emily and my son John

ISBN: 0-671-67973-2

First Pocket Books trade paperback printing June 1991

10 9 8 7 6 5 4 3 2 1

POCKET and colophon are registered trademarks of Simon & Schuster Inc.

Printed in the U.S.A.

In Hell...
Everyone Eats
Watermelon
NAKED

IF NOAH HAD BEEN A JEHOVAH'S WITNESS

MR. POTATO HEAD'S HELL

SHOPPER'S HELL

EINSTEIN DISCOVERS THE PROCESS
OF ELIMINATION

THE THREE BLIND MICE...
DRESSED ACCORDINGLY

SEX EDUCATION...TOUCAN, ONE CAN'T

HOMO SUCKUS ERECTUS...
A PREHISTORIC "YES" MAN

IF MICKEY HAD BEEN CREATED
BY SALVADOR DALI

NEW YORK...AFTER THE GREENHOUSE EFFECT

MR. POTATO...NOT QUITE GODUNOV

WHERE THEY REALLY FOUND THE TIN MAN

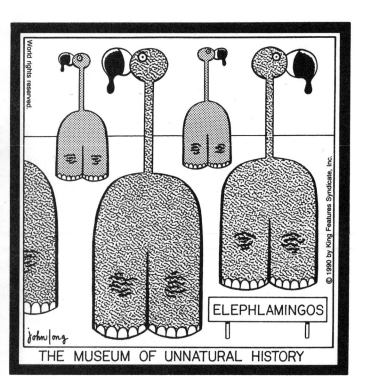

ELEPHLAMINGOS

THE MUSEUM OF UNNATURAL HISTORY

ACID SNOW

POTATOES SKINNY-DIPPIN'

BASHFUL – A BUYER FOR FREDERICK'S OF HOLLYWOOD.
DOC – PERFORMS LIPOSUCTION IN L.A.
HAPPY – A WRITER FOR THE MISTER ROGERS SHOW.
SNEEZY – ARRESTED FOR COCAINE POSSESSION.
GRUMPY – DRIVES A TAXI IN N.Y.C.
SLEEPY – OWNS A WATERBED STORE IN NEBRASKA.
DOPEY – A TELE-EVANGELIST IN ALABAMA.
SNOW WHITE – LAST SEEN WITH ROB LOWE.

THE SLEEZOID
WHATEVER HAPPENED TO THE SEVEN DWARFS?

THE SLAVE VOTE WAS UNANIMOUS

JUNIOR POTATO IS GOING TRICK-
OR-TREATING AS DARTH TATER

SOMETIMES...THE EARLY BIRD
GETS FROZEN STIFF

WINSTON'S BARK IS WORSE
THAN HIS BITE

EDUCATED GUESSES

THE MOOS BROTHERS' FIRST ALBUM
FOR MOOTOWN RECORDS

A DEFIANT WORM WEARING A HELMET,
SAFETY GLASSES AND A SEAT BELT

I YAM WHAT I YAM AND
THAT'S ALL THAT I YAM

wer ®
E MOVING

MAYFLOWER

MAYFLOWER BRINGS APRIL'S SHOWER

COMPOUND INTEREST?

GEORGE WASHINGTON WASN'T SO SMART...
IF HE WOULD'VE INVESTED THAT DOLLAR
HE THREW ACROSS THE DELAWARE, IT
WOULD BE WORTH $12,588,608 TODAY.

LITTLE SYBIL HAD A PROBLEM
WITH MULTIPLE PERSONALITIES

THE MUSEUM OF UNNATURAL HISTORY

FLEM PRACTICING ON HIS FLAMINGO

IF NOAH HAD BEEN AN INTERIOR DECORATOR

THE WICKED WITCH OF
THE NORTH POLE

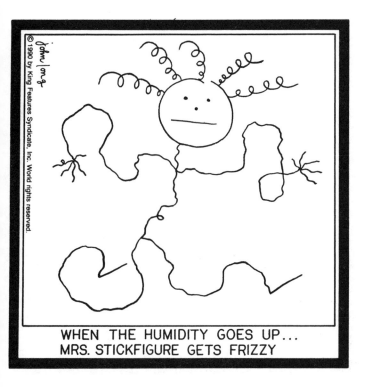

THE BIG BANANA THEORY OF EVOLUTION

EXCAVATION HAS REVEALED THE
PYRAMIDS TO ACTUALLY BE
LARGE PETRIFIED PLANTS

AN ARMORED COW...
WITH FAST-FOOD PARANOIA

COW PIE

BACH TO THE FUTURE

FLAMINGAROO
OR
← KANGAMINGO

THE MUSEUM OF UNNATURAL HISTORY

MR. DR. RUTH WESTHEIMER

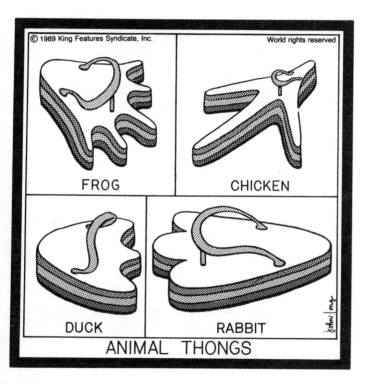

FROG

CHICKEN

DUCK

RABBIT

ANIMAL THONGS

HOPE

HOPE SPRINGS ETERNAL...AND SHE'S GETTING REAL TIRED OF IT

GIRIFFRAFF

VENUS FLY TRAP

MR. SNOWMAN KEEPS DROPPING HIS HOT COCOA

JCL-123

MERCEDES BENDS

CROSS A FLAMINGO WITH A COW AND YOU'RE TALKING HIGH STEAKS

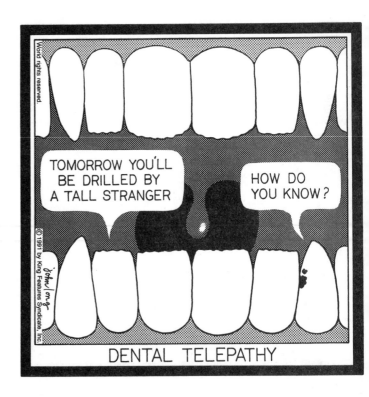

DENTAL TELEPATHY

THE SHAR-PEIS

RABBIT SCHOOL... CARROTS 101

BARB WEARING THE NEW ALL-NATURAL,
ANIMAL-FRIENDLY, FUR-BALL COAT

TO PREVENT WRINKLES MRS. POTATO
USES OIL OF FRITO LAY

SURE, THERE'S LIFE AFTER DEATH...
BUT ALL THE PAGES ARE STUCK TOGETHER

CRACK!

POCKET POOL

BIFF HAD A GRANDMOTHER WHO
PINCHED HIS CHEEKS EVERY
DAY FOR EIGHTEEN YEARS

I LIKE MANETS ON MY BLT

THE BABY PICTURE OF THE
BIRDMAN OF ALCATRAZ

IF NOAH HAD BEEN A WEATHERMAN

HOW INDIANS MAKE SNOWMEN

HERE'S ANOTHER SNOWBALL

HOW'S THE WEATHER, DEAR?

JUVENILE DELINQUENT ANTS

SISSY!

BEFORE YOU PLAY ANY MORE BASKETBALL... I WANT THOSE FINGERNAILS TRIMMED!

STREET BASKETBALL...NEW YORK CITY

FLAMINGOPHERS

THE MUSEUM OF UNNATURAL HISTORY

WHY MR. SNOWMAN RARELY BARBEQUES

JOEY, I TOLD YOU, "NEVER OPEN AN UMBRELLA INDOORS".

ZZZZZ

THIS SPACE FOR RENT

John Long

FLAMINGO PRACTICAL JOKES

STOCK ANSWER

UNCLE HILL... AUNT HILL

TAKING DRUGS IS LIKE MR. SNOWMAN
DRINKING HOT COCOA

THE REAL REASON THE EASTER BUNNY
BRINGS EGGS

MR. POTATO ENJOYS SOAKING IN THE TUB
UNTIL HIS SKIN GETS REALLY WRINKLED

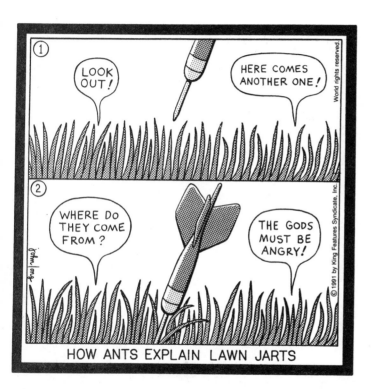

HOW ANTS EXPLAIN LAWN JARTS

MICHELANGELO PAINTING THE
SISTINE CHAPEL

MISTER ROGERS' HELL

ONE MAN'S HEAVEN IS ANOTHER MAN'S HELL

FLEM TENDS TO DO THINGS THE HARD WAY

MR. AND MRS. POTATO THOUGHT THEY
WERE STARTING TO LOOK ALIKE UNTIL
THEY DISCOVERED THAT THEY JUST
MIXED UP THEIR PARTS

ROBIN USING THE "CHIA PET"™
ATTACK MANEUVER

RIP VAN WINKLE AS A BABY

THE MASOCHIST'S HAMMER

SEXIST SNOWMAN

THE MUSEUM OF UNNATURAL HISTORY

MR. POTATO HEAD DOESN'T HAVE TO GO TO
THE DENTIST...HE JUST MAILS IN HIS MOUTH

THE GREAT NOAHLINI

IF NOAH HAD BEEN IN THE CIRCUS

THE CORRECT HAIRDO AND ACCESSORIES CAN HIDE MOST FLAWS

A JUNK-FOOD MONKEY

IN HELL...EVERYONE PLAYS THE ACCORDION

FOR OUR FIRST DATE ONE WOULD THINK THAT YOU'D BE A LITTLE MORE SENSITIVE AND WEAR FLATS.

A REAL LONELY ROBIN

SORRY ABOUT SPILLING THE HOT COCOA, MOM.

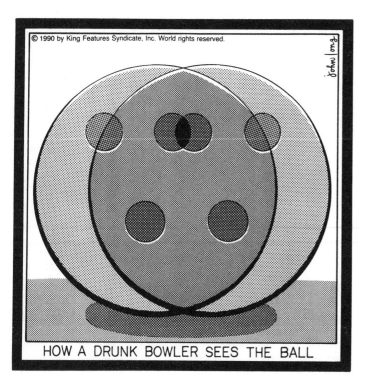

HOW A DRUNK BOWLER SEES THE BALL

THE ROBIN BEGAN TO GET SUSPICIOUS OF HER NEW NEIGHBOR

WILBER DOESN'T TRUST GRAVITY

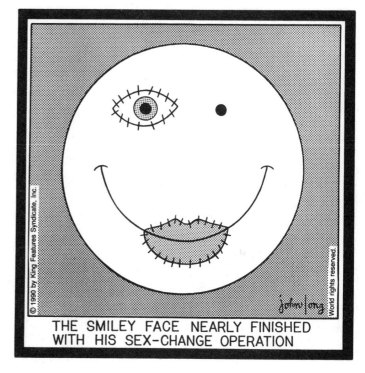

THE SMILEY FACE NEARLY FINISHED
WITH HIS SEX-CHANGE OPERATION

LAZY BOY

FLIES OF THE FUTURE

DON'T FLAMINGOS BUILD NESTS ON THE GROUND?

HOW MUCH IS INSTINCT...
HOW MUCH IS LEARNED

MR. STICKFIGURE WAS HIT BY A
BICYCLE WHEN HE WAS YOUNG

PIG WITH MUD FLAPS

NOMAD

SHAR-PEIOSAURUS REX

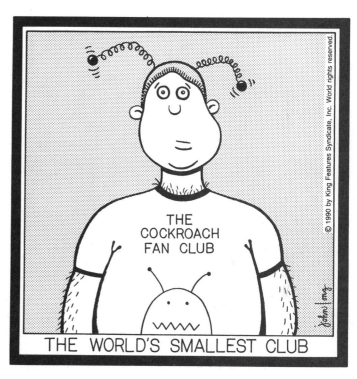

THE
COCKROACH
FAN CLUB

THE WORLD'S SMALLEST CLUB

SINCE FLEM WAS ON THE FOURTH FLOOR,
HE KNEW IT COULD ONLY BE...**COWZILLA!**

THE FISHNET WORKS ON
MR. FISH EVERY TIME

AN ARCHAEOLOGIST DISCOVERS AN OBVIOUS
SIGN OF POSSIBLE DINOSAUR REMAINS

IF EINSTEIN HAD BEEN A HEAVY DRINKER

WHY THE MOOSE BROTHERS SPLIT UP

LAWYER'S HELL

CAT'S HELL

FLEM'S STILL IN SHOCK...
HE RECEIVED A "CHIA PET", THE "CLAPPER", AND
THE "'SPORTS ILLUSTRATED'S' FOOTBALL PHONE"
FOR CHRISTMAS.

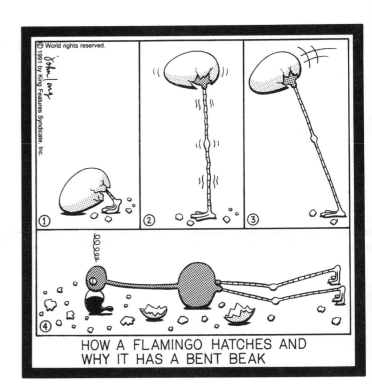

HOW A FLAMINGO HATCHES AND
WHY IT HAS A BENT BEAK

A NERDAROO

LOCATION IS EVERYTHING

TACKS WRITE OFF

MR. POTATO HAS SECOND THOUGHTS ABOUT BEING A GOALIE

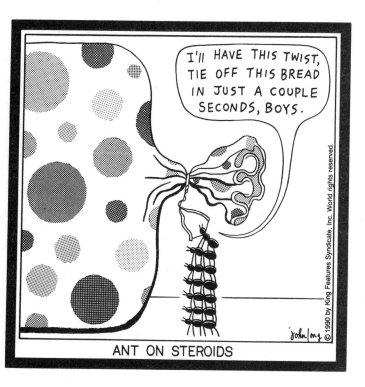

ANT ON STEROIDS

THE WICKED WITCH OF THE EAST COAST

KERMIT AND MISS PIGGY, NUDE

TRANSYLVANIA

PENCILVANIA

NOAH MEETS A GUY NAMED JOAH

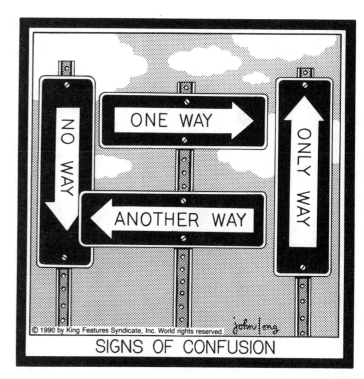

SIGNS OF CONFUSION

MR. AND MRS. POTATO TAKE JUNIOR
TO SEE KRIS PRINGLE

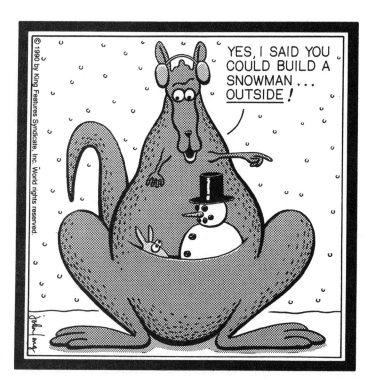

THE REAL REASON THE DINOSAUR BECAME EXTINCT...THE BIG-SNAP THEORY

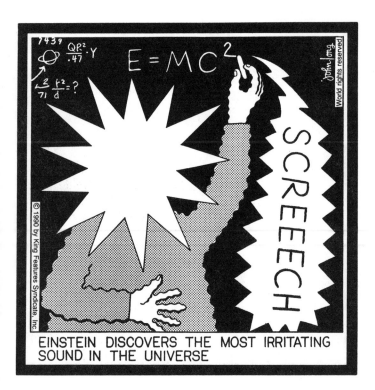

EINSTEIN DISCOVERS THE MOST IRRITATING
SOUND IN THE UNIVERSE

SNOWMEN FROM OTHER WORLDS

MR. SNOWMAN IS A LITTLE CONCERNED
ABOUT HIS NEW CAREER.

PLAYCOW

BULL WITH AN UDDER FETISH

FLEM FINALLY GOT TIRED OF PEOPLE ALWAYS SAYING..."GET A GRIP ON YOURSELF."

I NEED A VACATION

THIS IS MORE LIKE IT.

MR. POTATO HAS DECIDED TO QUIT HIS JOB AS A FIRE FIGHTER BEFORE HE BECOMES A BAKED POTATO

THE DALMATIAN IS UPSET BECAUSE NO ONE NOTICED HIS NEW SHIRT

RABBIT DREAMS

SAM'S ICE CHEST MAKES HIM
VERY POPULAR AT PARTIES

FLAMINGORILLA

THE MUSEUM OF UNNATURAL HISTORY

EVOLUTION AT WORK...

BEER

MAN WITH SNACK TRAY

OPERA SINGER

RENT ME

← DAY OR WEEK
INCLUDES STEREO
& OPERA ALBUMS

PLACEBO DOMINGO

DOOR #1 DOOR #2 DOOR #3

A SNOWBALL'S CHANCE IN HELL

LAWN SHARK

YOU REALLY FEEL STUPID WHEN YOU
REALIZE THAT YOU PLANTED YOUR
TULIP BULBS UPSIDE DOWN

GO AHEAD...TAKE MY JAY

A YOUNG GRANDMA MOSES

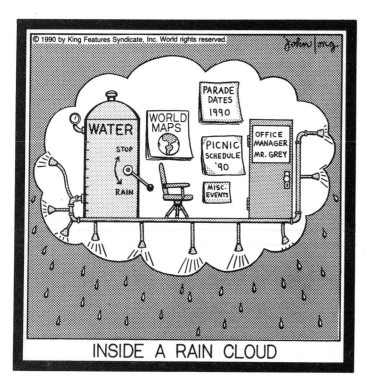

INSIDE A RAIN CLOUD

A POUCH POTATO

COMMENTARY BY THE MOOS BROTHERS

By now, for those of you who are keeping track, this is our third book and so you've probably figured out why John Long won the reputation as the "manic cartoonist from hell" from the guys over at King Features.

After all, we've been through HELLS from A to Z, HELLS of the rich, HELLS of the famous, HELLS of the not-so-famous, and even HELLS of inanimate objects. And from this we learn that everyone's HELL is different because everyone's OPINION about his or her HELL is different. It would be a pretty good bet that Dolly Parton's HELL would be a lot different from the HELL of the Pillsbury Dough Boy. This brings us to the issue as we see it. There could be a new opportunity in all this HELL business since all the zodiac stuff has gone the way of the mood ring. In fact . . . we think "WHAT'S YOUR HELL?" could be a real nice little ice breaker in your favorite social situation, perhaps while at your regular bar, laundromat, disco, or Piggly Wiggly. Imagine . . . just CHECK OUT everyone in the place and then ZERO IN on the most likely target. Instead of just sauntering over and dryly asking, "WHAT'S YOUR SIGN, BABE?," you cleverly say, "WHAT'S YOUR HELL, SWEETCHEEKS?" WELL . . . right off the bat . . . it's clear to your intended that you are SO SPECIAL . . . and BINGO . . . both of you could be in SYNC right away! If her (or his) HELL matches yours . . . just think . . . the rest is O-SO-EASY . . . AND . . . YOU BOTH WIN BIG PRIZES! All without the shallow and, might we add, expensive drudgery of dinners, movies, concerts, and dates in general. WITH OUR PLAN both of you could easily and safely know IF you could get something COOKIN' . . . and WHEN!

We know this is probably a new concept and perhaps a little bizarre to most of our less adventuresome readers, and MAYBE it does have a few rough spots. But we still think it's a pretty cool idea. As with all really great ideas . . . give it some time . . . after all, before MADONNA came along no one had come up with a new use for underwear in over 2,000 years.

By the time you're ready for another trip to the LONG OVERDUE ZONE (remember, there's fun for the whole family), we will have all the bugs worked out of what we think will be the hottest concept in cleverly and safely interfacing in social situations.

the Moor Bros.